Ultimate Sticker Collection

How to use this book

Read the captions, then find the
sticker that best fits the space.
(Hint: check the sticker labels for clues!)

•

There are lots of fantastic extra
stickers for creating your own
scenes throughout the book.

DK | Penguin Random House

Written by Julia March and Rosie Peet
Edited by Rosie Peet and Victoria Taylor
Designed by Lisa Robb, James McKeag and Anna Pond

First published in Great Britain in 2019 by
Dorling Kindersley Limited
80 Strand, London, WC2R 0RL
A Penguin Random House company

19 20 21 22 23 10 9 8 7 6 5 4 3 2 1
001–312823–Jul/2019

Page design copyright © 2019 Dorling Kindersley Limited
DK, a Division of Penguin Random House LLC

Manufactured by Dorling Kindersley, 80 Strand,
London, WC2R 0RL, UK, under license from the LEGO Group.

A CIP catalogue record for this book
is available from the British Library

ISBN 978-0-2413-6375-1

Printed and bound in China

A WORLD OF IDEAS:
SEE ALL THERE IS TO KNOW

www.dk.com

D0188561

Harry and friends

Harry Potter is a talented young wizard who studies magic at Hogwarts School of Witchcraft and Wizardry. He is loyal, brave and kind. These qualities have won him many friends in the classroom and beyond.

Harry Potter

On his 11th birthday, Harry was invited to attend Hogwarts. What a surprise! Until that moment, he hadn't even known he was a wizard!

Hagrid

Rubeus Hagrid is half-wizard, half-giant! He looks after the school grounds. He often uses a pink umbrella as a wand.

Ron

Ron Weasley is Harry's friend. He comes from a well-known wizarding family. Ron loves jokes and is also very brave – unless he sees a spider!

Hermione

Hermione Granger is one of Hogwarts' brainiest students – and she knows it! Hermione is friends with both Harry and Ron.

Dumbledore

Many years ago, Albus Dumbledore was a teacher at Hogwarts. Now, he is the school's headmaster. He is very old and very wise.

Fawkes

Fawkes is Dumbledore's pet phoenix. This magical bird cries tears that heal. When he gets old, he is reborn in a burst of fire.

Hogwarts Express

All aboard the Hogwarts Express!
This magical red train whisks Harry, Ron
and Hermione non-stop from London
King's Cross to Hogsmeade Station,
ready for a new term at Hogwarts school.

Platform sign
Each September 1st,
the train leaves from
platform 9¾ at 11 a.m.
A sign tells travellers
where to board.

Hidden entrance
New travellers quickly
learn how to find platform
9¾. They must run at a
hidden door in a wall!

KING'S CROSS

9

HOGWARTS CASTLE

HOGWARTS EXPRESS

5972

5972

Eager reader

Newspapers are sold from a kiosk on the platform. Hermione buys one. Harry is on the front page!

Best friends

Harry finds Ron and Hermione on platform 9¾. He is excited to see his best friends again after the long summer break!

Newspaper

Reading helps pass time on the journey. *The Daily Prophet* has all the latest news in the wizarding world.

The Hogwarts Express looks just like a traditional Muggle steam train.

Ready to go

Ron has packed everything he needs for the new term at Hogwarts. He's even remembered to bring his pet rat, Scabbers.

Journey to Hogwarts

Harry and his friends find a cosy compartment on board the Hogwarts Express. Time to sit back, relax and look forward to another year at Hogwarts. A highlight of the journey is snacking on sweets from the trolley!

Trolley witch

A friendly witch sells the passengers magical sweets from a trolley. She loves brightening up everyone's journey.

Full steam ahead

"Hogwarts Express" is printed on the front of the train. The destination, Hogwarts castle, is shown on the side.

The train passes through beautiful countryside on its way to Hogwarts.

HOGWARTS RAILWAYS

Magical feast

Harry and Ron buy some of everything and share it between them. Scabbers hopes they'll share some treats with him, too.

Bubble gum

Drooble's Best Blowing Gum is magical gum that never loses its flavour. It's great for blowing enormous bubbles!

Chocolate Frog

These sweet treats are a favourite among Hogwarts students. You have to be quick to eat them before they hop away!

Travelling teacher

The friends first meet Professor Lupin on the train. Hermione enjoys chatting with him about spells to protect against Dark magic.

5972

HOGWARTS CASTLE

Whomping Willow

The Whomping Willow grows on the grounds of Hogwarts. This fierce tree "whomps" anyone who comes close, attacking them with its branches. When Harry and Ron accidentally crash a flying car into the willow, the furious tree hits back!

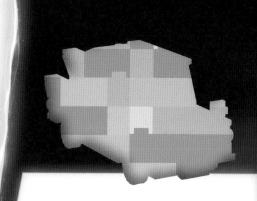

Flying Ford

This flying car is an enchanted Ford Anglia that belongs to Ron's dad, Arthur Weasley. It's hard to steer, as Harry and Ron find out.

Harry and Ron cling on as the angry tree tries to shake them to the ground!

Car trip

When Ron and Harry realize they've missed the train to school, they decide to fly there in the car. What could go wrong?

Severus Snape

Professor Snape is furious that Harry and Ron used magic outside school. He wants them expelled!

Tough tree

You'll never see any wildlife perched on the Whomping Willow's branches. Birds that try to nest there get whomped!

Secret tunnel

Under the tree is a secret tunnel. Ron should stay away – it leads straight to the spooky Shrieking Shack!

Argus Filch

Argus Filch is the strict school caretaker. It is Filch who takes Ron and Harry to Snape for their punishment. Filch does not like it when school rules are broken!

The Great Hall

At Hogwarts, students and teachers gather in the Great Hall to dine, receive owl post, and hear or make announcements. This lofty hall is also where new students are sorted into their Hogwarts houses.

Floating candles

The Great Hall is lit by magical candles that float in midair. They are drip-free, so nobody gets candle wax in their soup!

Students from rival houses meet in the Great Hall at mealtimes. Sometimes, arguments break out!

Sorting time

Professor McGonagall presides over the Sorting Ceremony. New students must put on the Sorting Hat to find out which house they will be in.

Sorting Hat

The clever Sorting Hat figures out the character of each student. Then, it shouts out the student's new house. The Hat never changes its mind!

House banners

Brightly coloured wall banners represent the four houses: Gryffindor, Slytherin, Hufflepuff and Ravenclaw.

Turkey leg

Students are served three meals a day in the Great Hall. Tasty turkey legs are always popular. Magic is hungry work!

Sweet treat

Ron loves cake, but he loves his rat, Scabbers, too. He is happy to share his sweet treat with his pet.

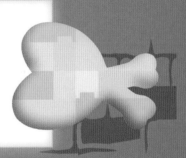

Thirst quencher

What better way to wash down a meal than a mug of pumpkin juice? Susan Bones sips hers at the Hufflepuff dining table.

Gryffindor House

Only the bravest students are sorted into Gryffindor. Students from other houses might say there is a fine line between being brave and being a showoff! Gryffindor students, including Harry, sometimes get into trouble for bending the rules.

Godric Gryffindor

Godric Gryffindor was one of the four founders of Hogwarts. He prized bravery, determination and loyalty in his students.

Argus Filch patrols the corridors at night. Mischievous Gryffindors are sometimes caught out of bed after dark!

Dormitory buddies

Harry and Ron share a room in the Gryffindor boys' dormitories. They often stay awake at night talking about their adventures.

Gryffindor crest

The Gryffindor colours are scarlet and gold. Students proudly wear ties and scarves in their house colours.

Neville Longbottom

Neville sometimes lacks confidence in his magical abilities. He is a loyal friend and bravely stands up for what is right.

Hermione's house

The Sorting Hat nearly put Hermione in Ravenclaw house. In the end, her great courage earned her a place in Gryffindor.

Seamus Finnigan

Seamus is a friendly Gryffindor. His spells sometimes backfire on him, making him accidentally blow things up!

Dean Thomas

Dean grew up in the Muggle world. He loves football, but since coming to Hogwarts his new favourite sport is Quidditch!

Other Houses

Harry, Hermione and Ron are all Gryffindors. But what about the rest of the students? Are they smart Ravenclaws, ambitious Slytherins or loyal Hufflepuffs? Only the Sorting Hat can decide!

Slytherin Crest

The Slytherin house crest is green and silver. The coiled serpent represents cunning, ambition and pride.

Draco Malfoy

Slytherin Draco Malfoy will stop at nothing to win. He thinks he's better than others because he is a pure-blood wizard.

Harry vs. Draco

Harry is a daring Gryffindor. Draco Malfoy is a cunning Slytherin. No wonder they keep clashing!

Salazar Slytherin, Rowena Ravenclaw and Helga Hufflepuff had different views on what makes a star student.

Luna Lovegood

Luna often seems to have her head in the clouds. However, like every other Ravenclaw student, she is focused when it comes to her studies.

Ravenclaw Crest

The Ravenclaw house crest features an eagle – a symbol of cleverness, learning and wisdom. Ravenclaw's house colours are blue and bronze.

Cho Chang

Cho plays Seeker for the Ravenclaw Quidditch team. She uses the school owls, like this tawny owl, to send letters home to her family.

Hufflepuff Crest

Hufflepuff students are loyal, honest and hardworking. Their house's crest shows a badger. Hufflepuff's house colours are yellow and black.

Susan Bones

Susan starts at Hogwarts at the same time as Harry. She is one of the first students to be sorted into a house. The Sorting Hat puts her in Hufflepuff.

Cedric Diggory

As captain of the Hufflepuff Quidditch team, Cedric makes sure his house always plays a fair game. He would rather lose than cheat.

Hogwarts at night

At night, the castle and its grounds are a spooky place to explore. Who – or what – might the students run into?

Use the extra stickers to create your own scene.

Meet the teachers

The professors at Hogwarts are experts in the subjects they teach. Their goal is to help each student reach their full potential. Some do this by gentle encouragement, while others take a stricter approach!

Madam Hooch

This flying instructor is also the referee for the Quidditch matches at Hogwarts. She blows her whistle at any sign of trouble.

Minerva McGonagall

Professor McGonagall is the Transfiguration teacher. She can turn a beetle into a button and back again in a flash!

Sybill Trelawney

Professor Trelawney teaches Divination, the art of predicting the future. Hermione thinks Trelawney makes up her predictions!

Filius Flitwick

Kind-natured Professor Flitwick has goblin ancestry. As well as teaching Charms, he also conducts the school choir.

Horace Slughorn

Slughorn is the Potions teacher in Harry's sixth year. He has a fondness for crystallized pineapple.

Rubeus Hagrid

Hagrid looks after the grounds at Hogwarts, including the Forbidden Forest and the fantastic creatures that live there.

Hogwarts School of Witchraft and Wizardry is a big place. It needs lots of teachers!

School lessons

Students at Hogwarts learn all the essential skills for wizarding life. Some, like Hermione, master new spells instantly. Some, like Ron, need to work a little harder. Every student has their own favourite lesson.

Laid-back learner

In class, Ron sometimes asks Hermione how to perform certain spells or how to correctly brew potions!

Potions

Students learn to brew magical potions down in the dungeons. Seamus Finnigan has a habit of making his potions explode!

Charms

This subject teaches students how to enchant various objects. Hermione uses a levitation charm to make this feather float.

Herbology

In Herbology, students learn all about magical plants, like this Mandrake. The Mandrake's cry is deadly, so Neville wears earmuffs for protection.

High flyer

Harry finds that he has a talent for flying during his first lesson. Playing Seeker for the Gryffindor team is his favourite part of life at Hogwarts.

Flying lessons

Flying can be tricky. Sometimes it is difficult to make your broom do what you want it to do! Susan Bones is starting to get the hang of it.

Care of Magical Creatures

Learning how to look after magical creatures can be scary. Draco Malfoy doesn't like the look of this big spider!

As head of Slytherin house, Professor Snape often favours Slytherin students in Potions class.

Castle secrets

Hogwarts was built many centuries ago. It is full of mysterious rooms containing strange magical objects. Not even Dumbledore himself knows everything about this ancient castle.

House ghosts

Hogwarts is home to several ghosts. The Gryffindor ghost, Nearly Headless Nick, likes to surprise students by appearing out of nowhere.

Invisibility Cloak

Students are not supposed to leave their rooms at night. Harry uses his Invisibility Cloak to explore the castle after dark.

House-elves

Dobby the house-elf visits Hogwarts with his masters, the Malfoys. Harry frees him with a sock! Dobby is so grateful to Harry that he helps him whenever possible.

Pensieve

Dumbledore keeps a special bowl called a Pensieve in his office. He stores his memories inside it when his mind has too many thoughts!

Harry wants to be part of a family. When he looks into the Mirror of Erised he sees himself with his parents.

Ron's wish

The Mirror of Erised reflects what you want most in the world. When Ron looks in the mirror, he sees himself as a Quidditch champion!

Warm socks

Dumbledore says when he looks in the mirror, he sees himself holding a pair of warm socks. The drafty castle can be chilly.

Moving stairs

Finding your way around Hogwarts can be tricky. The staircases like to move around. Sometimes they even disappear, leaving only a wall!

The Forbidden Forest

The deep, dark forest near Hogwarts is out of bounds to students – with good reason! Strange creatures lurk there. When Harry and Ron venture in, they soon meet Aragog, an enormous talking spider with a hungry family to feed.

Aragog's lair

Ferns, mushrooms and twisted tree roots surround Aragog's lair. Harry and Ron nearly get caught in a big, sticky web!

Nervous Ron

All these scuttling spiders make Ron nervous. Having a lantern does not make him happier about heading into the dark forest!

Jumping spider

Aragog has dozens of children, and they are all hungry. When they see Harry and Ron, they jump about in excitement.

Aragog

Aragog is a huge Acromantula spider. Is he a fierce monster or a gentle giant? Harry isn't sure!

Brave Harry

Brave Harry faces Aragog. He explains that he and Ron are friends of Hagrid, Aragog's only ally.

Trail of spiders

Harry and Ron followed this trail of spiders to Aragog's lair. There are so many, it's hard not to step on them!

Dark Arts

Magical arts designed to harm or hurt are known as the Dark Arts. They include mixing poisonous potions and raising dangerous beasts. At Hogwarts, students attend Defence Against the Dark Arts lessons to help them battle these dangerous forces.

Lord Voldemort

This master of Dark Arts is the most evil wizard ever. People call him "You-Know-Who", because they are too afraid of him to even say his name!

Professor Quirrell

Teacher Quirinus Quirrell is clever but weak-willed. Voldemort offers him power if Quirrell works for him.

Dementors are Dark creatures that suck the joy out of people. Lupin will banish this one with a Patronus Charm.

Tom Riddle's diary

Long ago, student Tom Riddle studied the Dark Arts. He made his diary into a Horcrux – an object that holds a piece of its owner's soul.

Mad-Eye Moody

Alastor Moody lost an eye battling the Dark Arts when Voldemort was first in power. He replaced it with a magical eye that can see through objects.

Basilisk

The Basilisk is a giant snake. This sinister serpent is very dangerous. It has venomous fangs and a fatal stare.

Boggart

Boggarts take the shape of your worst fear. Neville's Boggart looks like Snape! Picturing Snape wearing his grandmother's clothes makes Neville laugh and helps him defeat the Boggart.

Professor Umbridge

Dolores Umbridge is cruel and unpopular as a Defence Against the Dark Arts teacher. She refuses to teach her students how to defend themselves.

Playing Quidditch

Quidditch is an exciting team sport played entirely on flying broomsticks. Tournaments are hotly contested between the Hogwarts houses. Quidditch players must be swift, agile and tough. It's rough out there!

Golden Snitch

The Golden Snitch is a flying ball that dodges and darts around the pitch. If a Seeker catches it, the game is over.

Lucian Bole

Lucian plays for Slytherin as a Beater. Beaters must club away balls known as Bludgers. Lucian often clubs other players, too!

Sly Malfoy

Draco Malfoy was given a place on the team after his father bought expensive new broomsticks for all the Slytherin players.

Marcus Flint

The intimidating Slytherin captain, Marcus Flint, tries to unnerve opponents before a match. He is also known for using dangerous fouls.

Harry the Seeker

Harry is Gryffindor's youngest Seeker in 100 years. The Seeker has a special role in their team – to capture the Golden Snitch.

Goal!

A team's Chasers try to hit a ball called a Quaffle through one of their opponents' goal hoops. Each goal scores ten points.

Oliver Wood

Oliver is captain of the Gryffindor team. His rousing speeches and tough training regimes have led to many victories for his house.

Quidditch is played high in the air. Spectator towers give fans from each house the best possible view.

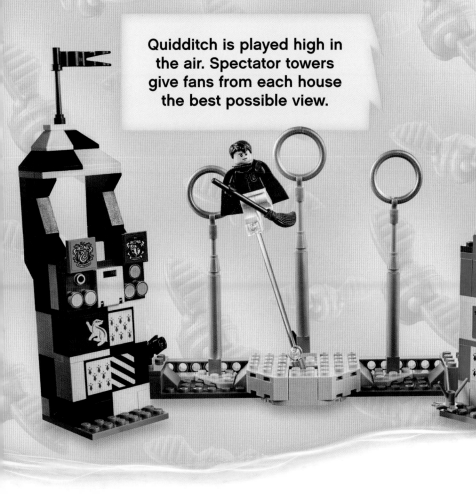

Play on!

Anything can happen in a match. Will anyone cheat? Who will catch the Snitch? The crowd watches eagerly!

Use your extra
stickers to create
a Quidditch scene.

RAVENCLAW

Animal friends

Unlike at most schools, Hogwarts students are allowed to bring animals! The most popular animals are owls, cats, toads and rats. They are helpful and friendly companions for young witches and wizards.

Crookshanks

Crookshanks is Hermione's pet cat. Like Hermione, he is very clever. He can sense when somebody is untrustworthy.

Hedwig

Harry's devoted owl was a birthday gift from Hagrid. Hedwig delivers Harry's post to him in the mornings.

Scabbers

Ron's rat, Scabbers, has been in his family for years. He is a little scruffy, but Ron is fond of him.

Trevor

Trevor the toad is Neville's pet. Trevor sometimes gets lost, but Neville's friends always help find him again.

Harry Potter

Madam
Hooch

Hidden entrance

Jumping
spider

Car trip

Magical feast

Sorting time

Gryffindor crest

Slytherin crest

Ravenclaw crest

Hufflepuff crest

Flying lessons

High flyer

House-elves

Trail of spiders

Lord Voldemort

Platform sign

Floating candles

Hagrid

Harry vs. Draco

Minerva McGonagall

Travelling teacher

Tough tree

Godric Gryffindor

Aragog

Oliver
Wood

Potions

Warm socks

Professor
Umbridge

Ron

Full steam
ahead

Flying Ford

Best
friends

Luna
Lovegood

Filius
Flitwick

House banners

Dormitory buddies

Charms

Pensieve

Marcus Flint

Aragog's lair

Boggart

Hermione

Cedric
Diggory

Thirst quencher

Tom Riddle's
diary

Neville
Longbottom

Rubeus
Hagrid

Severus
Snape

Hedwig

Trolley witch

Care of Magical Creatures

Newspaper

Brave
Harry

Mad-Eye Moody

Harry the Seeker

Moving stairs

Dumbledore

Bubble gum

Sweet treat

Seamus Finnigan

Crookshanks

Horace Slughorn

House ghosts

Cho Chang

Secret tunnel

Eager reader

Scabbers

Nervous Ron

Herbology

Sly Malfoy

Laid-back learner

Professor Quirrell

Chocolate Frog

Ron's wish

Sybill Trelawney

Hermione's house

Sorting Hat

Argus Filch

Fawkes

Ready to go

Draco Malfoy

Goal!

Trevor

Lucian Bole

Dean Thomas

Turkey leg

Susan Bones

Invisibility Cloak

Golden Snitch

Basilisk

EXTRA STICKERS

© LEGO 2019 ™ & © WBEI

© LEGO 2019 ™ & © WBEI

© LEGO 2019 ™ & © WBEI

© LEGO 2019 ™ & © WBEI

© LEGO 2019 ™ & © WBEI

© LEGO 2019 ™ & © WBEI

© LEGO 2019 ™ & © WBEI

© LEGO 2019 ™ & © WBEI

© LEGO 2019 ™ & © WBEI

© LEGO 2019 ™ & © WBEI

© LEGO 2019 ™ & © WBEI

© LEGO 2019 ™ & © WBEI

© LEGO 2019 ™ & © WBEI

© LEGO 2019 ™ & © WBEI

EXTRA STICKERS

EXTRA STICKERS

© LEGO 2019 ™ & © WBEI
© LEGO 2019 ™ & © WBEI
© LEGO 2019 ™ & © WBEI
© LEGO 2019 ™ & © WBEI
© LEGO 2019 ™ & © WBEI
© LEGO 2019 ™ & © WBEI
© LEGO 2019 ™ & © WBEI
© LEGO 2019 ™ & © WBEI
© LEGO 2019 ™ & © WBEI
© LEGO 2019 ™ & © WBEI
© LEGO 2019 ™ & © WBEI
© LEGO 2019 ™ & © WBEI
© LEGO 2019 ™ & © WBEI
© LEGO 2019 ™ & © WBEI
© LEGO 2019 ™ & © WBEI
© LEGO 2019 ™ & © WBEI
© LEGO 2019 ™ & © WBEI
© LEGO 2019 ™ & © WBEI

EXTRA STICKERS

EXTRA STICKERS

EXTRA STICKERS

EXTRA STICKERS